TIGER

HUGO

SUZY

BONNIE

JULIAN

PUNKINHEAD

STRIPE

TIGER®
TURNS ON

by BUD BLAKE

BOOKS

Grosset & Dunlap, Inc.
A NATIONAL GENERAL COMPANY

A TEMPO BOOKS *Original*

FIRST PRINTING, FEBRUARY 1970

TIGER.

TURNS ON

HUGO, CAN YOU HAMMER OUT THE DENT IN MY DOLL CARRIAGE?

I'LL GIVE YOU AN ESTIMATE — TEN CENTS FOR THE DENT AND FORTY CENTS FOR NEW WHEELS

NEW WHEELS? I DON'T NEED NEW WHEELS!

YOU WILL AFTER I HAMMER OUT THE DENT!

5-13 BUD BLAKE

BUD BLAKE

7-4